Barney's Song

I love you, you love me

We're a happy family!

With a great big hug,

And a kiss from

Me to You

Won't you say

You love me too?

Barney™

Contents

name : Lynn and Kate

Published by Pedigree Books Limited
Beech Hill House, Walnut Gardens, Exeter, Devon EX4 4DH.
E-mail books@pedigreegroup.co.uk
Published 2005

Pedigree®

£6.99

C is for Christmas - the best time of year
For Barney and friends to sing Christmas cheer!

H is for holly all covered in berries,
A wreath on the door makes Christmas more merry!

R is for reindeer who pull Santa's sleigh,
Delivering toys before Christmas Day.

I is for ice-skating on cold, icy lakes,
A winter wonderland of dazzling snowflakes.

S is for sleigh bells that jingle-a-ling,
A sleigh ride with friends is such a fun thing!

T is for toys in Santa's big sack,
Like dolls, bats and balls, and blocks you can stack.

M is for mistletoe hanging over the door,
With a hug and a kiss from a friend you adore.

A is for angel with bright, shiny wings.
Hush! If you listen, you might hear her sing.

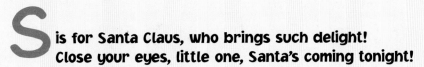

S is for Santa Claus, who brings such delight!
Close your eyes, little one, Santa's coming tonight!

Colouring Fun

Do you know these colours?

What colours will you use in your picture

Cleaning Up Song

Clean up! Clean up!

Toys and games are everywhere.

Clean up! Clean up!
Pick up, clean up, do your share!

What kind of animal is Baby Bop brushing?

Clean up! Clean up!

Scrub and brush and do your share!

Clean up! Clean up!

All pet owners everywhere.

15

Everyone is having fun in the garden.
Who is holding the rake?

Clean up! Clean up!
Garden workers everywhere.

Clean up! Clean up!
Rake it, bag it, do your share!

17

Clean up! Clean up!
All car washers everywhere.

18

Answer: Pink

Clean up! Clean up!

Scrub and shine and do your share!

19

Clean up! Clean up!

All shopkeepers everywhere.

Clean up! Clean up!

Pick up, sweep up, do your share!

BJ and Baby Bop are eating doughnuts.
How many doughnuts are left in the box?

Clean up! Clean up!
Cooks and bakers everywhere.

Clean up! Clean up!

Wipe up, mop up, do your share!

Clean up! Clean up!
Building workers everywhere.

Clean up! Clean up!

Lift and haul and do your share!

26

Clean up! Clean up!

Rubbish recyclers everywhere.

Clean up! Clean up!

Lift it, dump it, do your share!

Clean up! Clean up!
Everybody everywhere.

Clean up! Clean up!
Everybody do your share!

It is bath time everywhere.

Clean up! Clean up!
It is bath time everywhere.

30

Clean up! Clean up!
Wash and rinse and do your share!

31

Clean up! Clean up!
Everybody everywhere.

Clean up! Clean up!
Everybody do your share!

33

All clean! Sleep tight.

Thanks for helping do your share!

Let's Count

Count the items in each box.
Then trace over the answer.

2

5

Draw 1 big
hand and
1 small hand
on this clock.

Point to the
number 6.

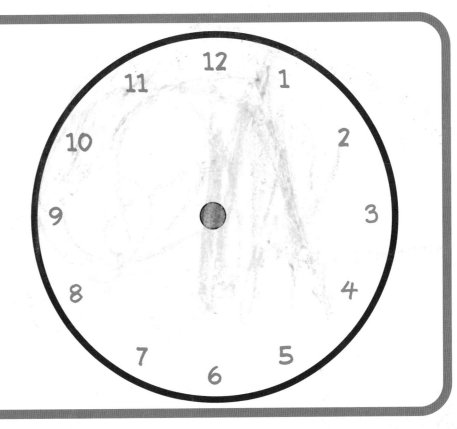

Welcome to the farm!
How many chicks can you count?

Farmer Barney had a dog
And Bingo was his name, oh.

Answer: 6

B-I-N-G-O
B-I-N-G-O
B-I-N-G-O

And Bingo was his name, oh.

**Farmer Barney had a dog
And Bingo was his name, oh.**

Answer: Cat

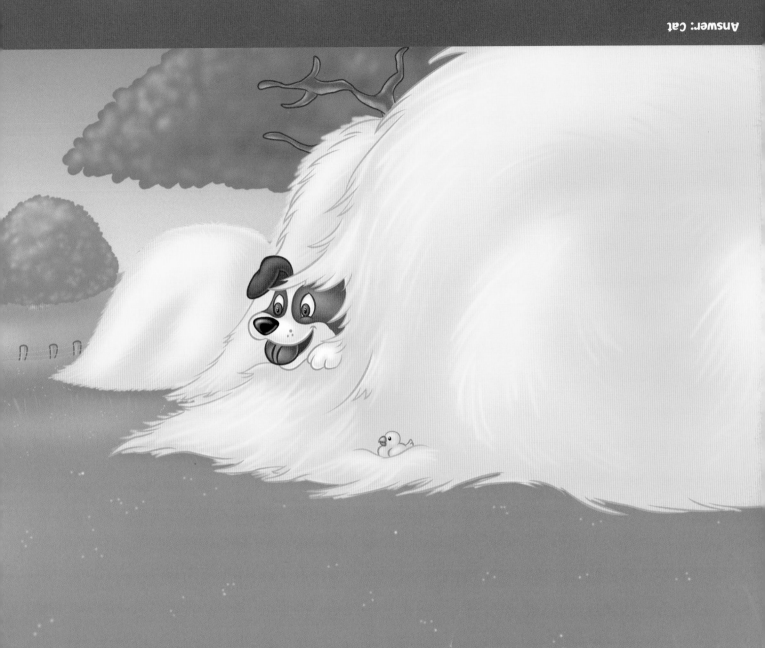

39

Everyone is running fast!
What colour is Bingo's collar?

And Bingo was his name, oh.

Answer: Red

MEOW-I-N-G-O

MEOW-I-N-G-O

MEOW-I-N-G-O

41

Farmer Barney had a dog

And Bingo was his name, oh.

And Bingo was his name, oh.

MEOW-RIBBIT-N-G-O
MEOW-RIBBIT-N-G-O
MEOW-RIBBIT-N-G-O

Farmer Barney had a dog
And Bingo was his name, oh.

Answer: 7

Bingo is running past the apple tree. How many apples have fallen on the ground?

And Bingo was his name, oh.

MEOW-RIBBIT-QUACK-G-O
MEOW-RIBBIT-QUACK-G-O
MEOW-RIBBIT-QUACK-G-O

Farmer Barney had a dog
And Bingo was his name, oh.

And Bingo was his name, oh.

Answer: 3

MEOW-RIBBIT-QUACK-OINK-O
MEOW-RIBBIT-QUACK-OINK-O
MEOW-RIBBIT-QUACK-OINK-O

Farmer Barney had a dog
And Bingo was his name, oh.

And Bingo was his name, oh.

Can you spot a chick hiding?

And Bingo was his name, oh.

How Many?

Colour a circle for each item in each box.
The first one has been done for you.

2 newspapers

4 books

3 clocks

1 wrist watch

Colour It In

Do you know these **colours**?
Which other **colours** will you use?

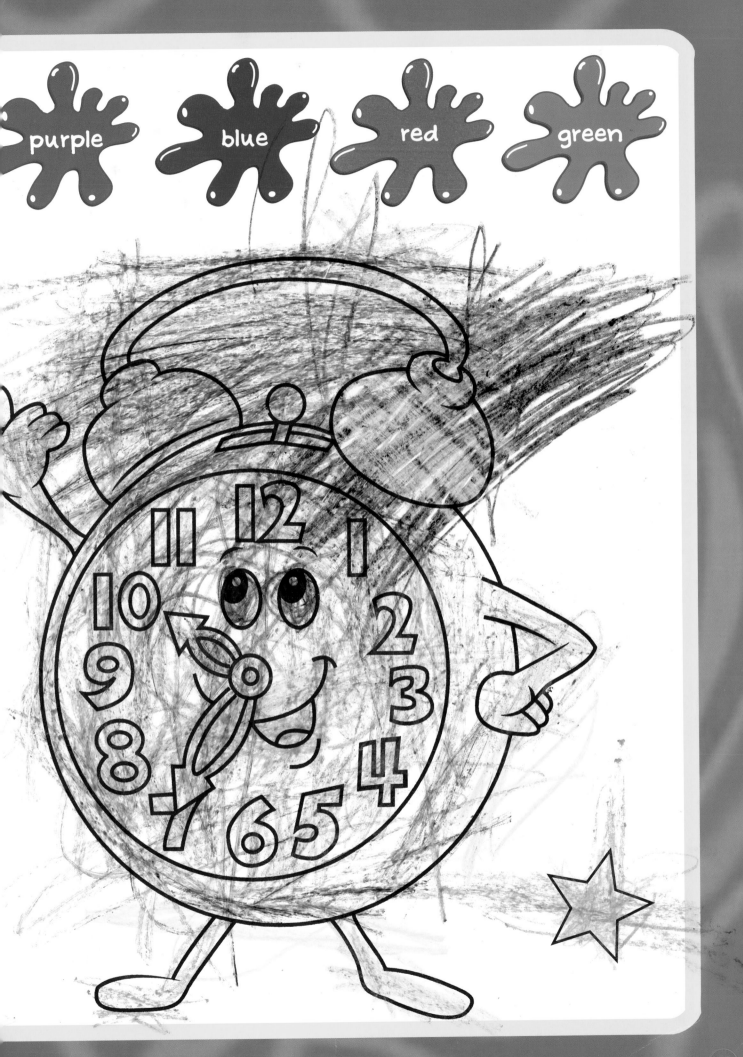